Acknowledgment

The first person I have to thank is Marguerite Henry because if she
hadn´t written *Misty of Chincoteague*, I might never have known
about this amazing island.

I also must thank my husband for understanding how much I wanted
to go to Chincoteague ever since I was a kid and saying, "Let´s go,"
when I mentioned it. Thank you to my children for letting me share
my dream with them, loving going on adventures with me,
and giving me purpose in life.

I would also like to thank my best friends, Ashley and Jes,
for listening to my crazy idea about writing a book and not only
encouraging me but also giving me advice and opinions
when I was stuck.

Lastly, I have to thank my amazing publishing team,
who made the whole process so easy and never thought
I had a dumb question since everything was new to me.

About the Author

Jessica MacPherson was born and raised in Massachusetts but always aspired to travel. Having completed a few road trips, growing up and into adulthood has been so much fun. There´s something about driving and finding places off the beaten path that are so unique and unforgettable.
Jessica enjoys going on all sorts of adventures and trips with her family and telling stories of her experiences.

Where the Wild Ponies Swim

Written by Jessica A. MacPherson
Illustrated by Red Maylon

For my children,
Josephine (Josie), Marcus, and Francesca (Frankie).
And to my husband, Brandon,
for always supporting me.

Mommy and Daddy took my brother, Marcus, my sister, Josie, and me, Frankie, on a road trip to see some wild ponies over the summer!

We drove from our home in Massachusetts through Connecticut, New York, New Jersey, Delaware, Maryland, and finally Virginia, where the island is. It took All. Day. Long.

It was a very long drive. We had to make many stops to go potty, eat, and stretch our legs. I was not happy when we had to get back into the car each time.

Josie would sing and play with me, and Marcus would make faces at me while Mommy would also try to give me toys.

Around dinner time, we finally arrived
on the small island called Chincoteague,
and we were so excited
to get out of the car
and explore the house!

The room we would be staying in
had something called "bunk beds,"
where Josie and Marcus
slept way up high on the top,
and I slept on the bottom.

These beds were so cool,
and I sometimes enjoyed
climbing the ladder up to the top.

The next day was Pony Swim Day!
We were so excited to be able to watch
the wild ponies swim over.
After breakfast, we dressed
and walked down to Pony Swim Lane.

Daddy had me on his shoulders while
he, Mommy, Josie, and Marcus attempted to
walk through the marsh to see the ponies swim over.

The marsh was so sticky and deep that Josie and Marcus couldn't do it,
and Daddy and Mommy would't let me
down into it. So, we walked back to the house to hose off.

After cleaning up, Mommy hung our dirty clothes on the deck
when the neighbors asked if we'd like pier passes so we could
go on their dock and watch the swim without getting dirty.

Mommy and Daddy kept saying thank you to our new friends
Greg and Lissa, and we were all delighted and excited
to be able to try again!

Once we all got into clean clothes, we headed over.
There was even a little mini beach next to the pier
where Daddy let me, Josie, and Marcus play
while waiting for it to be time
to watch the ponies.

Finally, the Coast Guard set off a red flare at slack tide, which meant it was time to go! Way off in the distance, the Saltwater Cowboys herded the ponies to the edge of the marsh on Assateague. Once they were all gathered and there were no stragglers, the ponies swam across.

There were a couple boats on either side of them, making sure they swam in the right direction to get to the marsh on the Chincoteague side.

It was so fun to watch them swim over and then eat the yummy marsh grass right next to us.

The ponies got to rest for a bit and gather some strength while eating before the Saltwater Cowboys marched them down Main Street toward the carnival grounds.

That night, when the carnival was open, we got to go
and see all the ponies that swam across that day.
We also got to have a lot of fun at the carnival.

Since Josie is the biggest,
she went on all the rides with Mommy.
I got to go on the carousel with Mommy, Josie, and Marcus.

We had some yummy carnival food, too.
Josie and Marcus got something called "cotton candy"
that I tried for the first time. I wasn´t sure if I liked it or not.

The next morning was Auction Day for the ponies!
This is where they show off each Pony, and people get to bid
if they want to buy one. They also have ponies called "buybacks."
This is when you bid on a pony, but it goes back to Assateague
to help keep the population and certain bloodlines going.
We did not bid as we don´t have anywhere to keep a Pony,
and the buybacks usually produce the most money,
but we got to watch everyone else.

The bidding can be intense, and they raised lots of money for
the Chincoteague Fire Department!

That night was an extra special night as the Governor and First Lady of Virginia came by to have a bill signing that declared the Chincoteague Pony the official state Pony of Virginia.

The following morning,
the buybacks and the rest of
the ponies not sold were marched
back down Main Street and to
Pony Swim Lane to swim back
to Assateague for another year.

That was the day we drove back home to Massachusetts,
so it was another long drive that
I was not looking forward to.

We had a great vacation and even enjoyed other parts of the island.

I hope we return sometime, maybe when I´m older and don´t mind the long car ride as much.

Printed in the USA
CPSIA information can be obtained
at www.ICGtesting.com
JSHW041620130124
55346JS00002B/3